The Autum EARTHQUAKE

by Mark Falstein illustrated by B. Gita

Chapters

Harcourt

Orlando   Boston   Dallas   Chicago   San Diego

Visit *The Learning Site!*

www.harcourtschool.com

It Starts!

I remember that afternoon well!

It began as an ordinary day at school. I went to my classes and talked and joked with my friends, just like always. I never guessed how the day would end.

When my brother Vic and I got home, I checked in with the Yens next door, just as Mom had asked me to. She had a doctor's appointment and would be home late.

Then I went to my room to do my homework. I had a whole page of math problems to do. I felt a compulsion to finish them, because I had to fix dinner. We were going to have hamburgers, my favorite.

Vic was cleaning his room and watching TV. I could hear a cartoon show through the door.

I had the radio on. I always think better with music playing. I was doing my last story problem, as the announcer read the news. It was a Tuesday, just after five o'clock.

When the rumbling started, I thought it was a truck passing on the street at first. Then it got louder. Maybe it's a low-flying airplane, I thought.

Then the house began to shake as if some giant had picked it up and was playing with it. Some of my books fell off my bookshelf. Uh-oh, I told myself. I was afraid I knew what was happening. This could be bad.

The announcer stopped talking. Then he said, almost in disbelief, "This is an earthquake, isn't it?"

I heard Vic yell just as the power went off. It was a good thing the sun hadn't gone down yet. I could still see pretty well.

I felt as if I was climbing a hill as I groped toward the door. A *moving* hill.

"Vic, get under the big table!" I yelled.

"Mommy!" he wailed.

I pulled Vic under the table. In an earthquake, you're supposed to get under something solid. A doorway is best. But the hallway to the front door seemed like a huge expanse of open area. A big crack could open up in the floor and engulf us before we got to the doorway.

I hugged Vic until long after the shaking ended.

As we huddled under that table, I thought of the earthquake drills we often had at school. I had hardly paid attention to them. They hadn't seemed real. This was real enough!

I knew there was a routine you were supposed to follow. What should I do first?

The gas line. You were supposed to shut off the gas in case the line was broken during the earthquake.

"Vic, come with me." I hoped he couldn't hear my voice waver.

"I'm scared," he said, crying softly.

"Then you'll have to stay here while I go."

"No!" He scrambled to his feet and followed me next door to the Yens' apartment.

Checking for Damage

I told Mr. Yen about turning off the gas. All three of us went to the basement. I found the lever, and Mr. Yen pulled it. No one in the building would be able to cook until the gas line was checked, but at least there wouldn't be an explosion.

Back upstairs, I checked the water in our apartment. It was running. There didn't seem to be any damage to the apartment. Then I tried the phone, but it wasn't working.

We went across the street to Aziz's Market. I bought batteries for the radio and flashlights. I also bought snacks that wouldn't need cooking or refrigeration.

Several neighbors were on the street, talking to each other. Someone had a radio on. I couldn't see much damage in our neighborhood, but the announcer was saying that part of the Bay Bridge was down. Across the bay in Oakland, a main road had collapsed.

Where was Mom's doctor? I couldn't remember. Not in Oakland, I hoped.

Sirens wailed in the distance. Smoke was rising not far to the west, beyond the hill near our house.

"Come on," I said to Vic. "Let's take a walk."

We walked up the hill. From the top, we could
see across the expanse of San Francisco. No
cracks had opened to swallow up the city. But
there were buildings on fire to the west, past the

PARK HOURS
6AM TO 8PM

library. On Franklin Street a brick front had
fallen off a house. Traffic was a mess everywhere
we could see.

Waiting for Mom

"Listen," I said to Vic. "We're just going to follow our regular routine, all right? I'll fix you a peanut-butter sandwich and some milk for supper. Then I'll read you some books until Mom gets home."

"OK," said Vic. "She'll be home soon, right?"

"Sure," I said, trying to hide my worry.

Back home I tried not to panic. Darkness was falling, so I had to read to Vic by flashlight. The news was grim, but I needed to keep the radio on. I was glad Vic didn't really understand what was happening. It seemed like an adventure to him now.

Then I heard a soft thumping on the ceiling.

"That's Mrs. Jaynes!" I said. "She may need help!"

Ada Jaynes was 93 years old. I hadn't thought of her until that moment. Now I didn't hesitate. I grabbed the key we kept to her apartment, and Vic and I dashed upstairs.

"Mrs. Jaynes!" I called as I unlocked her door.
"Mrs. Jaynes!" Vic echoed.

Inside, I heard a faint cry from one bedroom.
"Back there!" I told Vic.

Mrs. Jaynes had fallen during the earthquake.
"I'm all right. I'm all right," she said as I helped
her up. "I know I don't have any bones broken.
But my china—just look at it! My mother's china,
which came all the way *from* China!" she said in
anguish.

I helped Mrs. Jaynes down to our apartment. I thought we would all feel better if we were together.

"Let's make her some tea!" Vic said.

"That's a nice idea, but there's no gas for cooking," I said.

"Let's build a campfire!"

"I don't think so, Vic," I said.

"Thank you, Carin and Vic, for coming to my rescue," Mrs. Jaynes said. "I don't know how long I might have lain there if you hadn't helped me."

I was glad we had been able to help her.

Still Waiting

We decided to have milk and cookies, which was fine with Vic. Other neighbors stopped by to check on us. They told us there had been almost no damage to their apartments, either.

Mr. Yen checked the gas line. It seemed OK, but we had to wait for the fire department to turn the gas back on. If there was a break in the line, the gas fumes might engulf us.

As Mr. Yen was leaving our apartment, he put his hand on my shoulder. "Carin," he said, "you did so well when the earthquake first started. You must have paid attention to those earthquake drills at school."

"I guess I did," I said. Still, I wished Mom had been there to tell us what to do. Where was she?

As it grew darker outside, Mrs. Jaynes told us that she had been a little girl in San Francisco during the great earthquake of 1906. Nearly 3,000 people had died in that quake, including some of her neighbors. About 28,000 buildings were destroyed. She and her family had to move out of their home until it could be repaired.

I looked around at our safe, quiet apartment and was very thankful.

But where was Mom? There was the smell of smoke in the air. I could hear sirens as ambulances and fire trucks rushed to emergencies. I crossed my fingers, hoping that they weren't hurrying to help Mom.

Finally the apartment door opened, and Mom rushed in. She was out of breath and hurried to hug Vic and me.

"Thank goodness you're both all right! I tried to call you, but I couldn't find a phone that was working."

Then she let us go and smiled. "I was in the doctor's office when the quake hit, and the lights went out!" she said. "I had to get dressed in the dark and walk down nine flights of stairs. The buses aren't running, so I walked all the way home! Actually, I was so worried about you two that I ran part of the way."

We all laughed. We were glad we were safe. I knew we all had stories we would tell for a long time to come.